On a Train

Written by Roderick Hunt and Annemarie Young

Illustrated by Nick Schon,
based on the original characters
created by Alex Brychta

OXFORD
UNIVERSITY PRESS

The children were excited. They were going to France on a train. Gran was taking them to EuroParc near Paris.

Kipper was a bit worried.
"Everyone speaks French in
France," he thought. "I can't
speak French."

First they had to catch a train
to London. Mum and Dad were
going with them to see them off
at St Pancras Station.

The train arrived and Dad said,
"Press that button when it lights up.
It will open the doors. Then we'll
find a seat."

In London, they went down a long escalator to an Underground station.

"We're going down to the Tube train now," said Gran.

"Look," said Gran. "There's the roller-coaster at EuroParc."

"It looks scary," said Kipper.

The train came and they got on.

They soon arrived at St Pancras
International Station.

"Look at that roof!" said Biff.
"It's huge."

"It's time to say goodbye," said Mum. "You must check in and find your seat on the Eurostar."

"Enjoy yourselves," said Dad.

"Wow!" said Kipper. "Is this
our train?"

"Yes," said Gran. "Our seats
are in carriage 10."

Gran put her case in the
luggage bay.

"Let's look for our seats,"
said Chip.

They found their seats, but a man
and a little girl were sitting in them.

"I think these seats are ours,"
said Gran.

"Pardon!" said the man. He was
French. "I am sorry," he said. "Our
seats must be on the other side of
the aisle. We must move, Emily."

The man smiled at the children.
"Is your grandmother taking you
to EuroParc?" he asked.

"How did you guess?" asked Biff.

"Ah!" laughed the man. "I live nearby. Emily likes to stay with me, so she can visit EuroParc every day."

"Can Emily sit with us, please?"
asked Biff.

"Then she can teach us to speak
French!" said Kipper.

Emily sat with the children and
Monsieur Simon sat with Gran.
The train began to move out of
the station.

The train picked up speed very
quickly. Soon it went into the tunnel
under the English Channel.

"My ears went pop," said Kipper.

"Bonjour is hello in French," said
Emily. "But don't worry. Everyone
speaks English at EuroParc."

"Pardon?" said Kipper.

In Paris they caught a special
train called The EuroParc Express.
"This is the fourth train we've
been on today," said Chip.

The next day they met Emily and
her grandfather at EuroParc.

"Bonjour," said Kipper.

"Bonjour!" said Emily.

"I'd like a ride on that
roller-coaster," said Gran.
"Who's coming?"

"Not me!" said Kipper. "I'll show
you the ride I want to go on."

"What is it?" asked Gran.

"Not another train!" laughed
Gran. "Aren't you tired of trains?"
  "No way! I love trains," said
Kipper.

Talk about the story

What word did
Kipper learn to say
in French?

Which train
do you think Kipper
liked best?

Why do people
go on trains?

Where would
you like to go
on a train?

How to catch a train

Buy your ticket.

Check the display board to find the platform number.

Go and wait on the platform.

Wait for the train
to stop.

Press the button
to open the door.

Find a seat.

Stay close to the
grown ups you're with.

29

A maze

Help Kipper find the right train track
to take him home to Little Ted.